THE SONOMA DIET™

RECIPES

Meredith® BOOKS

Des Moines, Iowa

Copyright © 2008 Meredith Corporation
First Edition. Printed in China.
Excerpted from *The Sonoma Diet Recipes*, 2006.
ISBN: 978-0-696-24089-8

THE SONOMA DIET Recipes

Table of Contents

Welcome to The Sonoma Diet

The Sonoma Diet is like no other

The Sonoma Diet is designed to help you lose weight and gain health while you enjoy your meals more than ever before. It is a true food-lover's diet.

The emphasis of The Sonoma Diet is not to eliminate good food groups, like so many trendy diets. Rather, it will help you eat the best foods on the planet—foods that are rich in nutrients and instill vitality. Although The Sonoma Diet is based nutritionally on the healthful eating habits of the Mediterranean countries, it is inspired by the culinary creativity of California's Sonoma County, incorporating fresh, wholesome, great-tasting foods. The biggest difference between the Sonoma and Mediterranean diets, though, is the goal. The Sonoma Diet is a unique weight loss plan that allows you to enjoy tasty meals in the right portions without counting calories, fat, or points. No math is required and there are no charts to maintain.

Power Foods

The Sonoma Diet is not a low-carb, no-fat diet. It emphasizes foods that have been shown to have extraordinary health-promoting qualities. See the "10 Power Foods" chapter starting on page 6.

Catch the Wave

The Sonoma Diet is divided into three stages, or waves.

Wave 1 lasts 10 days. During this period you'll be overcoming your habit of consuming sugar, refined flour products, and other quickly absorbed foods that most likely led to your weight concerns in the first place. This is the only restrictive part of the diet.

During Wave 2 you'll continue developing the Sonoma approach to eating. Each meal is savored slowly with an emphasis on health and pleasure.

Wave 3 starts the day you reach your target weight. At this point, you will have mastered a healthful way of eating.

The Sonoma Diet Highlights

Decades ago, researchers started pondering a seeming paradox: Why do Mediterranean populations live healthier, longer lives with lower rates of heart disease, cancer, obesity, and diabetes compared to many parts of the world? The answer lies in the flavorful, nutrient-rich foods and "way of living" of the Mediterranean. Minimal processing and seasonal choices maximize the nutritional content of these foods. Now you can adopt a weight loss diet based on the Mediterranean way of eating.

The Sonoma Diet is all about . . .

BALANCE. It has nothing to do with low-carb or no-fat.

WHOLE GRAINS. You'll be eating bread and cereal from Day 1.

POWER FOODS. Generous amounts of delicious, nutrient-dense foods help you lose weight.

HEALTH. It's based on the Mediterranean diet, which has helped protect southern Europeans from heart disease and other killers for centuries.

PLEASURE. You'll slow down to savor and enjoy your meals, Sonoma style.

MOUTHWATERING RECIPES. Straight from the culinary masters of California's Sonoma country—simple, elegant, and delicious.

OLIVE OIL. This heart-healthy, nutrition-boosting, flavor-enhancing plant oil shatters the myth that dietary fat is evil.

Photographer: istockphoto.com/Monika Wisniewska

SIMPLICITY. You won't count calories or anything else. We did that for you.

VARIETY. You can pick and choose the foods you want each day from a variety of meats, seafood, fruits, vegetables, grains, and other food types.

PORTION CONTROL. When you fill your required plate or bowl, you'll be eating just the right amount of food.

FRESH WHOLE FOODS. The emphasis is on the sun-drenched, flavor-packed, nutrient-dense treats like those from Sonoma's farms and ranches.

WINE. Thank the Mediterraneans for showing us that a glass of wine at dinner enhances your heart health as well as your meal.

SATISFACTION. The meals are complete and keep you satisfied.

10 *Power Foods*

The Sonoma Diet *emphasizes foods shown to have extraordinary health-promoting qualities. These power foods are rich in essential nutrients and have the most nutritional benefits for the calories they provide. Many foods fit this description, but The Sonoma Diet has selected the top 10 power foods for you to help you plan your meals and lose weight.*

Phytonutrients

The power foods—fruits, vegetables, and whole grains—are packed with vitamins, minerals, and phytonutrients. Phytochemicals are plant chemicals that help keep plants healthy. They give the fruits and vegetables their unique color, flavor, and texture and provide us with phytonutrients.

Phytonutrients work best in conjuction with vitamins and minerals, so it is best to eat a variety of whole foods for the greatest health benefits. Phytonutrients are now thought to help protect people against disease and boost the immune system. Phytonutrients in the power foods work in many ways, but one stands out—their antioxidative action.

Antioxidants

Antioxidants protect the body from free radicals that cause damage to the cells. They are thought to help ward off heart disease and cancer, while keeping the immune system, the mind, and eyes in good shape.

1 *strawberries*

Bite them, slice them, smash them, or mix them—they're good no matter what you do.

WITH MODERN TRANSPORTATION AND STORAGE, STRAWBERRIES ARE AVAILABLE YEAR-ROUND. BUT THE BERRIES OF SUMMER ARE STILL THE BEST. USE FROZEN ONES THE REST OF THE YEAR.

WHEN BUYING FRESH STRAWBERRIES, CHOOSE ONLY THOSE BERRIES THAT ARE BRIGHT RED AND STILL HAVE THEIR STEM FIRMLY ATTACHED.

These juicy berries are a good source of vitamins B-2, C, and K. Strawberries have been shown to reduce inflammation in the body, which helps prevent heart disease and possibly rheumatoid arthritis.

2 *spinach*

Add spinach to pasta or rice and turn it into a gourmet dish.

Try fresh spinach right out of the bag, cleaned and packed for easy use.

COOK SPINACH
WITH ONION,
GARLIC, AND
YOUR FAVORITE HERB
FOR A QUICK, TASTY
SIDE DISH.

Popeye (the cartoon character) was right; spinach is the "power" food. Spinach is often recommended for overall health. Iron, calcium, and folate are just some of its nutrients.

3 Grapes

Who doesn't like grapes?
Green, purple, or red, they are sweet,
juicy, and refreshing.

For a delicious flavor and texture, add chilled grapes to your favorite pasta, chicken, or seafood salad.

GRAPES AND WINE ARE ONE OF THE BIG REASONS MODERN RESEARCHERS GOT CURIOUS ABOUT THE MEDITERRANEAN DIET TO BEGIN WITH.

GRAPES ARE TASTY, READY TO EAT ANYTIME AND ANYWHERE, AND AVAILABLE ALL YEAR. THEY ARE ONE OF MOTHER NATURE'S MOST CONVENIENT SNACK FOODS—JUST RINSE AND EAT.

They are high in sugar but loaded with nutrients. Enjoy a half-cup serving to get those phytonutrients working for your heart.

4 Broccoli

Flavor cooked broccoli with herbs and spices for variety and a colorful side dish.

BROCCOLI IS THE GOURMET POWER FOOD
FROM THE MEDITERRANEAN.

For the best flavor, steam broccoli until tender in a steamer or microwave with a couple of tablespoons of water. Do not overcook.

It is high in vitamins A and C, as well as calcium. A half-cup serving of cooked broccoli provides 40 mg of calcium and 1,700 IU of vitamin A.

5 Bell Peppers

Raw or cooked, they are versatile: tossed into salads or pasta, layered in sandwiches or casseroles.

PEPPERS OF ALL COLORS ARE LOW IN CALORIES AND LOADED WITH NUTRIENTS THAT ARE GOOD FOR THE HEART AND EYES, AND HELP PREVENT CANCER.

NOTICE THE SUBTLE FLAVOR DIFFERENCES WHEN TRYING THE DIFFERENT COLORS OF PEPPERS.

Peppers are high in vitamins A, C, B-6, and folate, as well as rich in antioxidants and phytonutrients.

6 whole Grains

Whole grains are the heart and soul of The Sonoma Diet.

WHOLE GRAINS ARE NOURISHING. BUT LIMIT THE AMOUNT YOU EAT TO ABOUT 25 PERCENT OF YOUR 9-INCH PLATE TO LOSE WEIGHT.

Whole grains boost metabolism and control blood sugar, helping to reduce your risk of diabetes, cardiovascular disease, and cancer.

READ CEREAL LABELS

☐ Whole grains should be listed as the first ingredient.

☐ Cereal should contain at least 2 grams of fiber per serving.

☐ Watch the sugar content (less than 3 grams per serving).

☐ Bran cereals can contain the most fiber of all whole grain choices, up to 8 grams per serving.

7 *Tomatoes*

Tomatoes are the classic heart-healthy Mediterranean food.

The most potent phytochemical in tomatoes is lycopene. Lycopene stimulates the immune function, may slow the effect of degenerative diseases, and reduces your risk of several cancers.

ADD TOMATOES TO COOKED VEGETABLES FOR ADDED FLAVOR AND TASTE.

IT'S EASY TO GET YOUR LYCOPENE, JUST SLICE OR CHOP TOMATOES INTO SALADS OR SANDWICHES.

Stock your pantry with canned tomatoes, sauces, and pastas.

8 Almonds

Toss toasted, sliced almonds on your salad or cereal.

TO BRING OUT THE FLAVOR OF RAW ALMONDS, TOAST THEM IN A MODERATE OVEN FOR A FEW MINUTES; COOL AND STORE IN AN AIRTIGHT CONTAINER.

Although high in calories, some studies have indicated that almonds did not lead to weight gain. Emerging research shows that eating almonds may play a role in weight maintenance or loss.

ALMONDS ARE CHOLESTEROL-FREE AND PACKED WITH VITAMIN E, MAGNESIUM, PROTEIN, FIBER, AND CALCIUM.

Research shows that eating 1 ounce (about a handful) of almonds each day may help lower LDL ("bad") cholesterol levels and raise HDL ("good") cholesterol levels.

9 olive oil

Drizzle olive oil dressing on your salad to bring out the flavor of the greens.

OLIVE OIL IS A TRUE WEIGHT LOSS BLESSING BECAUSE IT PROVIDES ESSENTIAL FATTY ACIDS WHILE ADDING FLAVOR TO ANY DISH.

Choose extra-virgin olive oil. It comes from the first pressing of the olives and has the greatest number of beneficial nutrients. It also has the most pleasing taste.

Providing antioxidants, monounsaturated fat, and vitamin E, olive oil is widely recognized for its heart-healthy benefits.

10 *Blueberries*

Blueberries are naturally sweet and delicious globes of goodness.

Fresh blueberries are at their best from May through October, when they are in season. Frozen blueberries are convenient and tasty throughout the year.

HIGH IN VITAMIN C AND FIBER, ENJOY THEM ONE AT A TIME OR TOPPED WITH PLAIN FAT-FREE YOGURT.

Blueberries are the champion of antioxidants. Along with reducing your risk of heart disease, certain cancers, and vision loss, they are also shown to reduce and possibly reverse memory decline that comes with aging.

How to Get Started on The Sonoma Diet

To begin, Sonoma-ize your kitchen. Get rid of all the refined white flour foods, chips, and sugared sweets. Discard any foods in the toss list and stock your pantry with the healthful ones.

TOSS...

- ☐ Sugar
- ☐ White bread, crackers
- ☐ Cookies, cake, candy, ice cream
- ☐ White rice
- ☐ Chips
- ☐ Mayonnaise, regular salad dressings
- ☐ Regular soda, fruit juices
- ☐ Jam, jelly, syrup
- ☐ Butter, margarine
- ☐ Regular cheeses and cream cheese
- ☐ Milk (except fat-free)
- ☐ Fatty meats (such as bacon or sausage)

STOCK...

- ☐ Vegetables low in starch and calories (such as green beans, bell peppers, broccoli, cabbage, greens, tomatoes)
- ☐ Whole grains (bread, cereal, pasta, brown rice)
- ☐ Lean meat, poultry, and fish
- ☐ Fat-free milk, yogurt, and low-fat cheeses
- ☐ Fruits (apples, berries, oranges, watermelon)
- ☐ Dried beans and legumes (chickpeas, black beans, tofu)
- ☐ Extra-virgin olive oil
- ☐ Healthful nuts (almonds, walnuts)

A NEW PLATE

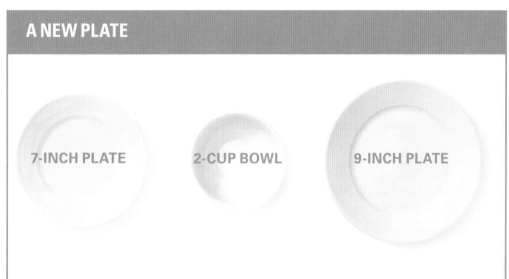

7-INCH PLATE   2-CUP BOWL   9-INCH PLATE

After you've restocked your kitchen, you have one more key purchase to make—dishware. You will eat from two specific plates and one specific bowl throughout your time spent on The Sonoma Diet—that is, through Waves 1 and 2.

Your breakfast plate must measure 7 inches from edge to edge; your lunch and dinner plate must measure 9 inches from edge to edge. Your breakfast bowl (for cereals with milk, for example) must hold exactly two cups of liquid—no less, no more.

The reason for these picky plate-size requirements is to ensure portion control. You'll be eating the right amount of food at each meal because only the right amount will fit on your plate. You don't count calories or grams or anything else. You just fill your plate or bowl with the recommended foods.

HOW YOU ALLOCATE THE FOOD ON YOUR PLATES VARIES BY WAVE. FOR ALL THE INFORMATION YOU NEED TO BE SUCCESSFUL, LOOK FOR THE BOOK *THE SONOMA DIET.*

Planning Wave 1 Meals

The purpose of Wave 1 is to give you a boost by starting off losing weight quickly, to get you going with your new healthful eating habits, and to reintroduce you to reasonable portion sizes.

That's a tall order, but it's all going to happen within 10 days. That's how fast the transition is. You're going to leave behind your old habits and start losing weight on Day 1.

The most important transition, though, will be to get you off the refined flour/white-bread/sugar caravan that has wreaked so much havoc with your metabolism. You have to get those bread-and-cake cravings out of your system. The only way to do it is cold turkey. You will stop eating refined sugar immediately. You must totally eliminate your sugar habit or you'll continue to crave sweets and you won't lose weight. Most artifically sweetened foods are forbidden in Wave 1, even though they don't have the same effect on your metabolism. There's a good reason for this. You won't lose your cravings if you continue to satisfy them, even with artificially sweetened foods. Even fruits are taboo on Wave 1 because of their high sugar content. The most important goal during Wave 1 is to break your sugar addiction.

Your vegetable choices are also more limited in Wave 1. Only very low-calorie and high-fiber vegetables are allowed. On both Wave 1 and 2 you may use 3 servings of fat per day as you see fit. A serving of fat is 1 teaspoon of olive oil, 11 almonds, or 14 peanuts.

Flexibility is the key. The recipes on the following pages are divided into Wave 1 and Wave 2 to simplify your decision-making. You can use the recipes and menus we have provided, or improvise and use your own recipes within the given guidelines.

Include 1 or 2 snacks per day to help you get through Wave 1. Wave 1 is the most restrictive part of your diet but remember it is only for 10 days. Only Wave 1 vegetables are included in the recipes to make choices easy. The only restriction on meat is that it should be low in fat. There is no restriction on flavor. Your meals will be interesting and satisfying.

STEAK SALAD WITH BUTTERMILK DRESSING

START TO FINISH: 35 MINUTES   **MAKES:** 4 SERVINGS

8   ounces boneless beef top sirloin steak
8   cups torn mixed salad greens
   Nonstick olive oil cooking spray
¼   cup finely shredded fresh basil
   Kosher salt (optional)
   Freshly ground black pepper (optional)
2   medium carrots, cut into thin bite-size strips
1   cup yellow and/or red pear-shape tomatoes, halved
1   medium red bell pepper, cut into thin bite-size strips
   Buttermilk Dressing (below)

1. If desired, partially freeze meat for easier slicing. Arrange salad greens on four dinner plates. Set aside. Trim fat from meat. Cut meat across the grain into thin bite-size strips.

2. Lightly coat an unheated large skillet with cooking spray; heat over medium-high heat. Add meat strips. Cook and stir for 2 to 3 minutes or until meat is slightly pink in center. Remove from heat. Stir in basil. Season to taste with kosher salt and black pepper.

3. To serve, spoon the warm meat mixture over greens. Top with carrot, tomato, and bell pepper. Drizzle with Buttermilk Dressing. Serve immediately.

PER SERVING: 171 cal., 4 g fat (2 g sat. fat), 40 mg chol., 381 mg sodium, 15 g carbo., 3 g fiber, 18 g pro.

Buttermilk Dressing: In a small bowl, combine ½ cup plain low-fat yogurt; ⅓ cup buttermilk; 3 tablespoons grated Parmesan cheese; 3 tablespoons finely chopped red onion; 3 tablespoons fat-free mayonnaise dressing; 2 tablespoons chopped fresh parsley or 1 teaspoon dried parsley flakes; 1 tablespoon white wine vinegar or lemon juice; 1 clove garlic, minced (½ teaspoon minced); ¼ teaspoon kosher salt; and ⅛ teaspoon freshly ground black pepper. Cover and chill for 30 minutes to 24 hours.

BRAISED HUNTER-STYLE CHICKEN

PREP: 30 MINUTES **COOK:** 20 MINUTES **MAKES:** 4 SERVINGS

4 **chicken breast halves (with bone) (1¾ to 2 pounds total)**
1 **tablespoon extra-virgin olive oil**
1 **cup sliced fresh mushrooms**
1 **cup chopped onion**
2 **cloves garlic, minced (1 teaspoon minced)**
1 **14½-ounce can stewed tomatoes, undrained**
¼ **cup dry red wine**
2 **tablespoons tomato paste**
1 **tablespoon finely chopped fresh thyme or 1 teaspoon dried thyme, crushed**
1 **bay leaf**
1 **tablespoon chopped fresh flat-leaf parsley**
1 **tablespoon lemon juice**
 Kosher salt
 Freshly ground black pepper

1. Remove skin from chicken. In a 12-inch skillet, heat olive oil over medium heat. Add chicken; cook until brown, turning to brown evenly. Remove chicken from skillet; set aside.

2. Add mushrooms, onion, and garlic to skillet. Cook for 8 to 10 minutes or until onion is very tender and lightly browned, stirring occasionally.

3. Add stewed tomatoes, wine, tomato paste, dried thyme (if using), and bay leaf to skillet. Bring to boiling; reduce heat. Return chicken to skillet. Simmer, covered, for 20 to 25 minutes or until chicken is tender and no longer pink (170°F).

4. To serve, transfer chicken to a serving platter. Discard bay leaf. Stir fresh thyme (if using), parsley, and lemon juice into tomato mixture. Season to taste with kosher salt and pepper. Serve tomato mixture over chicken.

PER SERVING: 243 cal., 5 g fat (1 g sat. fat), 75 mg chol., 364 mg sodium, 14 g carbo., 2 g fiber, 32 g pro.

LIGHT-STYLE TUNA SALAD

START TO FINISH: 15 MINUTES **MAKES:** 4 SERVINGS

⅓ cup reduced-calorie or fat-free Caesar salad dressing

2 teaspoons chopped fresh tarragon or ¼ teaspoon dried tarragon, crushed

1 10-ounce package mixed salad greens (about 8 cups)

1 large tomato, cut into thin wedges

1 6-ounce can chunk white tuna (water pack), drained and broken into chunks

1. In a small bowl, stir together salad dressing and tarragon; set aside.

2. To serve, arrange salad greens on four dinner plates. Top with tomato and tuna. Drizzle with dressing mixture.

PER SERVING: 121 cal., 5 g fat (0 g sat. fat), 22 mg chol., 557 mg sodium, 6 g carbo., 2 g fiber, 13 g pro.

SLOW DOWN AND SAVOR THE MEALS

Evidence shows that people gain more weight when they eat on the run or standing in front of the refrigerator than when they sit down to enjoy a meal. Other evidence shows that people who eat fast are prone to overeating because they're still bolting down food even though the stomach has sent a message to the brain that it's had enough.

Stress-free, pleasurable eating is at the heart of The Sonoma Diet. Savor, taste, and appreciate each bite of the delicious foods you eat. You can't do that in a hurry or while you are watching television. Slow down; make your meals a leisurely part of your life.

Start by promising yourself to eat at least one meal a day slowly, stresslessly, and pleasurably. Don't eat while rushing, don't eat on the run or standing up, and don't eat while watching television. Get used to eating slowly; you'll love it, and it will help you lose weight.

GRILLED SAGE PORK CHOPS

PREP: 20 MINUTES **GRILL:** 12 MINUTES **MAKES:** 6 SERVINGS

6 **boneless pork sirloin chops, cut ¾ inch thick**
   Kosher salt
   Freshly ground black pepper
2 **tablespoons soy sauce**
1 **tablespoon chopped fresh sage or 1 teaspoon dried sage, crushed**
1 **tablespoon extra-virgin olive oil**
4 **to 6 cloves garlic, minced (2 to 3 teaspoons minced)**
2 **teaspoons lemon juice**
1 **tablespoon chopped fresh sage or 1 teaspoon dried sage, crushed**
1 **tablespoon chopped fresh flat-leaf parsley**
1 **tablespoon lemon juice**
1 **tablespoon extra-virgin olive oil**

1. Trim fat from meat. Sprinkle with kosher salt and pepper. For basting sauce: In a small bowl, combine soy sauce, 1 tablespoon fresh or 1 teaspoon dried sage, 1 tablespoon oil, garlic, and 2 teaspoons lemon juice. Brush the top of meat with *half* of the basting sauce.

2. For a charcoal grill, place meat on the rack of an uncovered grill directly over medium coals. Grill for 12 to 15 minutes or until juices run clear (160°F), turning and brushing once with the remaining basting sauce halfway through grilling. Discard any remaining basting sauce. (For a gas grill, preheat grill. Reduce heat to medium. Place meat on grill rack over heat. Cover and grill as above.)

3. Meanwhile, in a small bowl, combine 1 tablespoon fresh or 1 teaspoon dried sage, the parsley, the 1 tablespoon lemon juice, and 1 tablespoon oil.

4. To serve, cut the meat into ¼-inch-thick slices. Top with parsley mixture.

PER SERVING: 257 cal., 12 g fat (3 g sat. fat), 94 mg chol., 489 mg sodium, 2 g carbo., 0 g fiber, 32 g pro.

BROCCOLI WITH LEMON AND DILL

START TO FINISH: 25 MINUTES   **MAKES:** 6 TO 8 SERVINGS

½ cup chopped onion or leek (white part only)
1 clove garlic, minced (½ teaspoon minced)
1 tablespoon extra-virgin olive oil
½ cup reduced-sodium chicken broth
1½ pounds broccoli, cut into spears
1 tablespoon lemon juice
½ teaspoon cornstarch
2 tablespoons chopped fresh dill or 1 teaspoon dried dill
Kosher salt
Freshly ground black pepper
Lemon slices (optional)

1. In a large saucepan, cook and stir onion and garlic in hot oil about 3 minutes or until tender. Add broth; bring to boiling. Add broccoli. Return to boiling; reduce heat. Cook, covered, for 8 to 10 minutes or until tender. Transfer vegetables to a serving bowl, reserving broth in saucepan (add additional broth, if necessary, to measure ½ cup).
2. For sauce: In a small bowl, stir together lemon juice and cornstarch; stir into broth in saucepan. Cook and stir until thickened and bubbly. Cook and stir for 2 minutes more. Stir in dill. Season to taste with kosher salt and pepper.
3. To serve, spoon sauce over vegetables; toss gently to coat. If desired, garnish with lemon slices.

PER SERVING: 53 cal., 3 g fat (0 g sat. fat), 0 mg chol., 151 mg sodium, 7 g carbo., 2 g fiber, 2 g pro.

CRUMB-TOPPED CAULIFLOWER

PREP: 25 MINUTES **BAKE:** 15 MINUTES **OVEN:** 375°F **MAKES:** 6 SERVINGS

¼ cup extra-virgin olive oil
3 cloves garlic, minced (1½ teaspoons minced)
4 cups cauliflower florets
3 tablespoons lemon juice
1 ounce thinly sliced prosciutto, cut into thin bite-size strips
2 tablespoons capers, drained
2 tablespoons chopped fresh flat-leaf parsley
1 tablespoon finely chopped anchovy fillets (optional)
  Kosher salt
  Freshly ground black pepper
1 cup soft whole wheat bread crumbs

1. Preheat oven to 375°F. In a large skillet, heat 2 tablespoons of the oil over medium heat. Add garlic; cook and stir for 30 seconds.
2. Add cauliflower; cook about 10 minutes or until tender, stirring frequently. Add lemon juice, prosciutto, capers, 1 tablespoon of the parsley, and, if desired, the anchovies. Cook and stir for 2 minutes more. Season to taste with kosher salt and pepper.
3. Transfer cauliflower mixture to a 2-quart square baking dish. In a small bowl, combine bread crumbs, the remaining 2 tablespoons oil, and the remaining 1 tablespoon parsley; sprinkle on top of cauliflower mixture.
4. Bake about 15 minutes or until bread crumbs are browned.

PER SERVING: 129 cal., 10 g fat (1 g sat. fat), 0 mg chol., 298 mg sodium, 7 g carbo., 2 g fiber, 3 g pro.

BEANS AND CARAMELIZED ONIONS

START TO FINISH: 20 MINUTES   MAKES: 5 SERVINGS

1 tablespoon extra-virgin olive oil
1½ cups chopped onion
1 tablespoon balsamic vinegar or red wine vinegar
½ cup bottled roasted red bell peppers, drained and finely chopped
¼ cup quartered pitted ripe olives
2 tablespoons chopped fresh basil or ½ teaspoon dried basil, crushed
¼ teaspoon kosher salt
¼ teaspoon freshly ground black pepper
1 pound fresh green beans, trimmed (if desired) and cut into 2-inch pieces (about 4 cups)

1. In a large heavy skillet, heat oil over medium heat. Add onion; cook about 10 minutes or until onion is very tender and golden brown, stirring occasionally. Stir in vinegar. Cook and stir for 1 to 2 minutes more or until liquid is evaporated. Stir in roasted bell pepper, olives, basil, kosher salt, and black pepper. Remove skillet from heat; cover and keep warm.

2. Meanwhile, in a covered medium saucepan, cook green beans in a small amount of boiling water for 10 to 12 minutes or until crisp-tender; drain. To serve, stir the onion mixture into green beans.

PER SERVING: 85 cal., 4 g fat (0 g sat. fat), 0 mg chol., 162 mg sodium, 13 g carbo., 4 g fiber, 2 g pro.

Planning Wave 2 Meals

This is the main part of your diet. You will stay with this eating plan until you reach your desired weight. Wave 2 keeps the weight loss going after the quick transition period of Wave 1. Planning what you will eat each day is easy using your new plate and bowl.

Whole grains and other foods high in fiber are staples of The Sonoma Diet. Fiber helps in weight loss by keeping you feeling full and satisfied longer. All 10 power foods (page 6) are now allowed. Almost all vegetables (except white potatoes) are allowed on this part of the diet. Fruits are part of the daily diet in Wave 2. You will be eating one fruit serving at both lunch and dinner. That makes following the diet much easier. One glass of wine is also a part of the diet, if you choose.

Flexibility is still the key. You can use the recipes given here or improvise and use your own within the guidelines. On Wave 2 you can use both the Wave 1 and 2 recipes given in this booklet.

As you plan your daily intake remember to include appropriate snacks. Snacks keep you from getting too hungry between meals as well as provide the needed nutrients.

Photographer: istockphoto.com/Monika Wisniewska

CHICKEN QUESADILLAS

START TO FINISH: 15 MINUTES   **MAKES:** 2 SERVINGS

1   **10-inch low-carb spinach or whole wheat flour tortilla**
    Nonstick olive oil cooking spray
½   **cup shredded reduced-fat cheddar cheese (2 ounces)**
½   **cup shredded cooked chicken breast or turkey breast (about 3 ounces)**
¼   **cup chopped avocado**
2   **to 3 small fresh jalapeño chile peppers, seeded and thinly sliced***
½   **cup purchased salsa**

1. Lightly coat one side of the tortilla with cooking spray. Sprinkle *half* of the cheese evenly on half the surface of the uncoated side of the tortilla. Top with chicken, avocado, and jalapeño pepper. Add a little of the salsa and sprinkle with the remaining cheese. Fold tortilla over filling.

2. Heat a heavy skillet or griddle over medium heat. Add quesadilla; cook for 2 to 4 minutes or until cheese is melted and tortilla is lightly browned, turning once. Cut into six wedges. Serve warm with the remaining salsa.

PER SERVING: 279 cal., 13 g fat (5 g sat. fat), 50 mg chol., 701 mg sodium, 17 g carbo., 10 g fiber, 22 g pro.

*Note: Because hot chile peppers contain oils that can burn your skin and eyes, wear rubber or plastic gloves when working with them. If your bare hands do touch the chile peppers, wash your hands well with soap and water.

CHICKEN-MUSHROOM PASTA

START TO FINISH: 30 MINUTES **MAKES:** 6 SERVINGS

- 8 ounces dried whole wheat penne pasta (2⅔ cups)
- 12 ounces skinless, boneless chicken breast halves, cut into bite-size strips
- ¼ teaspoon kosher salt
- ⅛ teaspoon freshly ground black pepper
- 2 tablespoons extra-virgin olive oil
- 4 cloves garlic, minced (2 teaspoons minced)
- 3 cups sliced fresh mushrooms (8 ounces)
- 1 medium onion, thinly sliced
- ½ cup chicken broth
- ¼ cup dry white wine
- 1 cup cut-up roma tomato
- ¼ cup shredded fresh basil leaves
- 3 tablespoons chopped fresh oregano or ¾ teaspoon dried oregano, crushed
- ¼ cup finely shredded Parmesan cheese (1 ounce)
- ⅛ teaspoon freshly ground black pepper

1. Cook pasta in boiling, lightly salted water according to package directions; drain. Return to saucepan; cover and keep warm.

2. Meanwhile, season chicken with kosher salt and ⅛ teaspoon pepper. In a large skillet, heat 1 tablespoon of the oil over medium-high heat. Add chicken and garlic; cook and stir about 5 minutes or until chicken is tender and no longer pink. Remove from skillet; cover and keep warm.

3. Add the remaining 1 tablespoon oil to skillet. Cook mushrooms and onion in hot oil just until tender, stirring occasionally. Carefully add broth and wine. Bring to boiling; reduce heat. Boil gently, uncovered, about 2 minutes or until liquid is reduced by about half. Remove skillet from heat.

4. Add cooked pasta, chicken, tomato, basil, and oregano to mushroom mixture; toss gently to coat. Transfer to a serving dish. Sprinkle with Parmesan cheese and ⅛ teaspoon pepper.

PER SERVING: 287 cal., 8 g fat (2 g sat. fat), 35 mg chol., 254 mg sodium, 34 g carbo., 4 g fiber, 22 g pro.

CHICKEN TOSSED SALAD

START TO FINISH: 20 MINUTES **MAKES:** 4 SERVINGS

- **4 skinless, boneless chicken breast halves (about 1¼ pounds total)**
- **1 tablespoon extra-virgin olive oil**
- **¼ teaspoon garlic-pepper seasoning**
- **8 cups torn mixed salad greens**
- **1 medium yellow or red bell pepper, cut into bite-size strips**
- **1 medium tomato, cut into wedges**
- **½ cup reduced-calorie berry or roasted garlic vinaigrette salad dressing**
- **¼ cup crumbled feta cheese (1 ounce)**
- **¼ cup whole wheat croutons (optional)**

1. Brush the chicken with olive oil; sprinkle with garlic-pepper seasoning. In a large nonstick skillet, cook chicken over medium heat for 8 to 10 minutes or until chicken is tender and no longer pink (170°F), turning once. Cut the chicken into bite-size strips. Set aside.

2. In a large serving bowl, combine salad greens, bell pepper, and tomato. Pour salad dressing over greens mixture; toss gently to coat. Top with chicken, feta cheese, and, if desired, croutons.

PER SERVING: 312 cal., 10 g fat (2 g sat. fat), 88 mg chol., 217 mg sodium, 20 g carbo., 2 g fiber, 36 g pro.

SONOMA SALMON BURGERS

PREP: 25 MINUTES **GRILL:** 8 MINUTES **MAKES:** 4 SERVINGS

   1   **pound fresh or frozen skinless, boneless salmon fillets**
   ¾ **cup sliced, pitted ripe olives**
   ¼ **cup chopped green onions**
   1   **tablespoon chopped fresh dill or ½ teaspoon dried dill**
   2   **teaspoons finely shredded lemon peel**
   ½ **teaspoon kosher salt**
   1   **tablespoon extra-virgin olive oil**
1½ **cups lightly packed arugula**
   ¼ **cup thinly sliced celery**
   1   **medium shallot, thinly sliced**
   2   **tablespoons lemon juice**
   2   **large whole wheat pita bread rounds, halved crosswise**
      Lemon wedges (optional)

1. Thaw salmon, if frozen. Rinse salmon; pat dry with paper towels. Cut salmon into pieces. Place salmon in a food processor. Cover and pulse with several on-off turns until salmon is coarsely ground. Transfer to a large bowl. Stir in olives, green onion, dill, lemon peel, and kosher salt. Shape salmon mixture into four ½-inch-thick patties. Brush both sides of each salmon patty with olive oil.

2. For a charcoal grill, place salmon patties on the rack of an uncovered grill directly over medium-hot coals. Grill for 8 to 12 minutes or until golden brown, carefully turning once halfway through grilling. (For a gas grill, preheat grill. Reduce heat to medium-high. Place salmon patties on grill rack over heat. Cover and grill as above.)

3. Meanwhile, in a small bowl, combine arugula, celery, shallot, and lemon juice. Set aside.

4. To serve, place salmon patties in pockets of pita bread halves. Divide arugula mixture among pita bread pockets. If desired, serve with lemon wedges.

PER SERVING: 362 cal., 19 g fat (3 g sat. fat), 67 mg chol., 708 mg sodium, 22 g carbo., 4 g fiber, 26 g pro.

PORK WITH APPLES IN CIDER SAUCE

PREP: 25 MINUTES **BAKE:** 20 MINUTES **OVEN:** 350°F **MAKES:** 4 SERVINGS

4 boneless pork loin chops, cut ¾ inch thick (1¼ to 1½ pounds total)
   Kosher salt
   Freshly ground black pepper
2 tablespoons extra-virgin olive oil
3 medium Granny Smith apples, peeled, cored, and cut into ½-inch-thick slices
1 cup reduced-sodium chicken broth
2 inches stick cinnamon
1 teaspoon cornstarch
1 teaspoon cold water

1. Preheat oven to 350°F. Trim fat from meat. Season meat with kosher salt and pepper. Set aside.
2. In a large skillet, heat the olive oil over medium heat. Add meat; cook for 4 to 6 minutes or until brown, turning once. Remove meat from skillet.
3. In the same skillet, cook and stir apple about 5 minutes or just until tender and browned. Carefully add broth and stick cinnamon. Cook and stir for 2 minutes. Using a slotted spoon, transfer apple to a 2-quart rectangular baking dish.
4. Place meat on top of the apple. Pour broth mixture over meat. Cover and bake about 20 minutes or until meat juices run clear (160°F). Remove meat from baking dish; cover and keep warm. Discard cinnamon.
5. Transfer the apple-broth mixture to a medium saucepan. Stir the cornstarch into the water; stir into apple-broth mixture. Cook and stir over medium heat until slightly thickened and bubbly. Cook and stir for 2 minutes more. Serve meat with apple-broth mixture.
PER SERVING: 308 cal., 14 g fat (3 g sat. fat), 89 mg chol., 357 mg sodium, 13 g carbo., 1 g fiber, 32 g pro.

TURKEY SOUP WITH BARLEY

PREP: 30 MINUTES **COOK:** 10 MINUTES **MAKES:** 4 SERVINGS

- 12 ounces turkey breast tenderloin or skinless, boneless chicken breast halves
- 1 tablespoon extra-virgin olive oil
- 1 medium onion, chopped
- 1/2 cup chopped red or green bell pepper
- 1 clove garlic, minced (1/2 teaspoon minced)
- 2 14-ounce cans reduced-sodium chicken broth
- 1 1/2 cups loose-pack frozen cut green beans
- 1 cup loose-pack frozen whole kernel corn or one 8-ounce can whole kernel corn, drained
- 1/3 cup quick-cooking barley
- 2 tablespoons chopped fresh basil or 1 1/2 teaspoons dried basil, crushed
- 1/4 teaspoon kosher salt
- 1/4 teaspoon freshly ground black pepper

1. Cut turkey into bite-size pieces. In a Dutch oven, cook and stir turkey in hot oil for 5 minutes. Use a slotted spoon to remove turkey from Dutch oven.

2. Add onion, bell pepper, and garlic to Dutch oven. Cook for 3 minutes, stirring occasionally. Drain off fat.

3. Return turkey to Dutch oven. Stir in broth, green beans, corn, uncooked barley, dried basil (if using), kosher salt, and black pepper. Bring to boiling; reduce heat. Cover and simmer for 10 to 15 minutes or until barley is tender. Stir in fresh basil (if using).

PER SERVING: 247 cal., 5 g fat (1 g sat. fat), 51 mg chol., 703 mg sodium, 25 g carbo., 4 g fiber, 26 g pro.

SPICY BLACK BEAN CHILI

PREP: 35 MINUTES **COOK:** 20 MINUTES **MAKES:** 4 SERVINGS

- 2 tablespoons extra-virgin olive oil
- 1 tablespoon cumin seeds
- 2 cups chopped onion
- ½ cup chopped green bell pepper
- 2 cloves garlic, minced (1 teaspoon minced)
- 2 15-ounce cans black beans, rinsed and drained
- 1 14½-ounce can diced tomatoes, undrained
- 1½ cups water
- 1 tablespoon chili powder
- 1 tablespoon chopped fresh oregano or 1 teaspoon dried oregano, crushed
- 2 teaspoons paprika
- ½ teaspoon crushed red pepper

  Kosher salt

  Freshly ground black pepper
- ½ cup thinly sliced green onion
- ¼ cup fat-free dairy sour cream or plain low-fat yogurt
- ¼ cup chopped fresh cilantro

1. In a large saucepan, heat olive oil over medium heat. Add cumin seeds; cook and stir for 1 minute. Stir in chopped onion, bell pepper, and garlic; cook and stir about 5 minutes or until onion is tender.

2. Stir in black beans, undrained tomatoes, the water, chili powder, dried oregano (if using), paprika, and crushed red pepper.

3. Bring to boiling; reduce heat. Simmer, uncovered, for 20 minutes. Stir in fresh oregano (if using). Season to taste with kosher salt and black pepper.

4. Top individual servings with green onion, sour cream, and cilantro.

PER SERVING: 296 cal., 8 g fat (1 g sat. fat), 3 mg chol., 799 mg sodium, 49 g carbo., 13 g fiber, 17 g pro.

MINTED FRUIT COMPOTE

START TO FINISH: 15 MINUTES **MAKES:** 6 SERVINGS

- 1 15¼-ounce can pineapple chunks (juice pack), drained
- 1 tablespoon finely slivered grapefruit peel
- 2 red grapefruits, peeled, halved lengthwise, and sliced ¼ inch thick
- 1 tablespoon finely slivered orange peel
- 2 oranges, peeled, halved lengthwise, and sliced ¼ inch thick
- 1 kiwifruit, peeled and sliced ¼ inch thick
- 1 to 2 tablespoons chopped fresh mint
- ¼ cup pomegranate seeds*
  Thinly sliced orange peel strips (optional)

1. In a large serving bowl, combine pineapple chunks, slivered grapefruit peel, grapefruit slices, slivered orange peel, orange slices, kiwifruit slices, and mint. If desired, cover and chill for 2 to 24 hours.

2. To serve, stir in pomegranate seeds. If desired, garnish with orange peel strips.

PER SERVING: 111 cal., 0 g fat (0 g sat. fat), 0 mg chol., 2 mg sodium, 28 g carbo., 4 g fiber, 2 g pro.

*Note: To remove pomegranate seeds, cut the fruit in half just through the skin. Remove the peel and break the fruit into sections. Use your fingers or a small spoon to separate the seeds from the membrane. Handle the fruit in a bowl filled with water; this allows the seeds to float to the top and prevents the juice from discoloring your hands. Discard the skin and membrane, and eat only the seeds.

PUDDING LOLLIPOPS

PREP: 20 MINUTES   **FREEZE:** 5 HOURS   **STAND:** 15 MINUTES
MAKES: 16 SERVINGS

- **1 4-serving-size package sugar-free instant chocolate or chocolate fudge pudding mix**
- **2 cups fat-free milk**
- **1 4-serving-size package sugar-free instant banana cream, butterscotch, pistachio, vanilla, or white chocolate pudding mix**
- **2 cups fat-free milk**

1. Place sixteen 3-ounce disposable plastic drink cups in a 13×9×2-inch baking pan; set aside.

2. In a medium bowl, combine chocolate pudding mix and 2 cups milk. Beat with a wire whisk or rotary beater about 2 minutes or until well mixed. Spoon *about 2 tablespoons* of the pudding into each cup. Cover each cup with foil; freeze for 1 hour.

3. In another medium bowl, combine banana cream pudding mix and 2 cups milk. Beat with a wire whisk or rotary beater about 2 minutes or until well mixed. Spoon *about 2 tablespoons* of the banana pudding over frozen pudding in each cup. Cover each cup with foil.

4. Use a sharp knife to make a small hole in center of foil. Push a wooden stick through the hole and into the top layer of pudding in the cup. Freeze for 4 to 6 hours or until pudding pops are firm.

5. To serve, let stand at room temperature for 15 to 20 minutes; remove pudding pops from cups.

PER SERVING: 36 cal., 0 g fat (0 g sat. fat), 1 mg chol., 194 mg sodium, 7 g carbo., 0 g fiber, 2 g pro.

Note: If you'd like, switch the order of the pudding in some of the cups. Start with the light-color pudding and top with the chocolate pudding.

Wave 3

Congratulations!

You have reached your desired weight. Now you want to maintain it. Wave 3 starts the day you reach your target weight. You feel great and you want to celebrate. Go ahead, you have earned it. You have eliminated sugar and refined flour from your diet. You are no longer dependent on fattening and unhealthy refined products. You are now using unsaturated fats and whole grains, and enjoy eating wholesome foods.

Most importantly, you have made the connection between eating for pleasure, eating for health, and eating to stay at your best weight. The food list now includes all fruits and vegetables. Continue to avoid high-fat meats and refined grains. Continue to use the Wave 2 guidelines to balance your diet. Enjoy your meals in a slow, satisfying way.

Keep the health and pleasure connection. Wave 3 is all about extending The Sonoma Diet lifestyle— you learned it to lose weight, now make it a permanent way of enjoying food and life.

Photographer: istockphoto.com/ Sean Locke